Meet Christ with Joy

Joan Brown SND

Preparation for First Communion

kevin
mayhew

Meet Christ with Joy

is a special book.
It is special because it is for you, as you prepare to
meet Christ for the first time in Holy Communion.

It is also for your family.

They will be able to share your preparation by joining
in the different activities, prayers and celebrations.

Meet Christ With Joy *is a different book, because*
most of it is still waiting to be written by **YOU**

_____

and by your family

_____

_____

_____

Go through the book in your own way, and share the
little celebrations (we sometimes call them 'liturgies')
with your family. Work out the way that suits you,
and them, best.

Parents please read the note on page 32

To Benjamin, my godson, and all children who, with this book, prepare to Meet Christ With Joy

First published in 1991 by KEVIN MAYHEW LTD
Buxhall, Stowmarket, Suffolk IP14 3BW
© 1991 Kevin Mayhew Ltd

ISBN 0 86209 172 1
Catalogue No 1425408

Illustrated by Natalie Bould

Families

Families come in all shapes and sizes

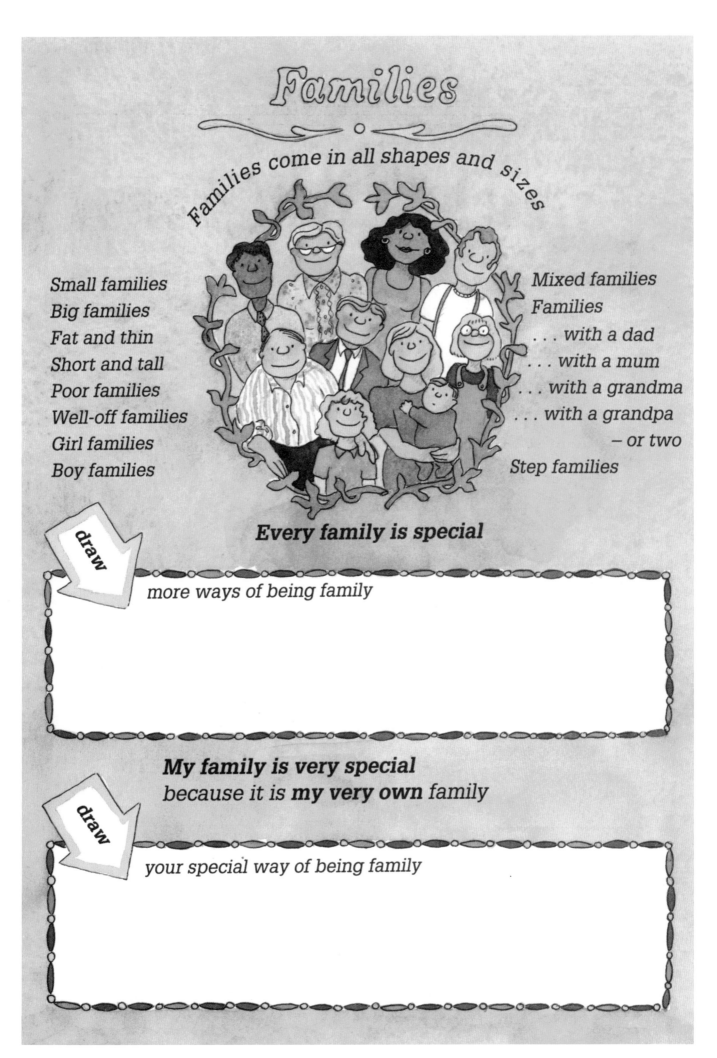

Small families
Big families
Fat and thin
Short and tall
Poor families
Well-off families
Girl families
Boy families

Mixed families
Families
. . . with a dad
. . . with a mum
. . . with a grandma
. . . with a grandpa
– or two
Step families

Every family is special

draw

more ways of being family

My family is very special
because it is **my very own** family

draw

your special way of being family

My Family

Colour in the houses

Stick in a family photo

My family name:

(colour it in)

Names of my family

_____

_____

_____

My family's special days:

_____

_____

_____

_____

My name is:

_____

I came into my family on:

_____

My special day

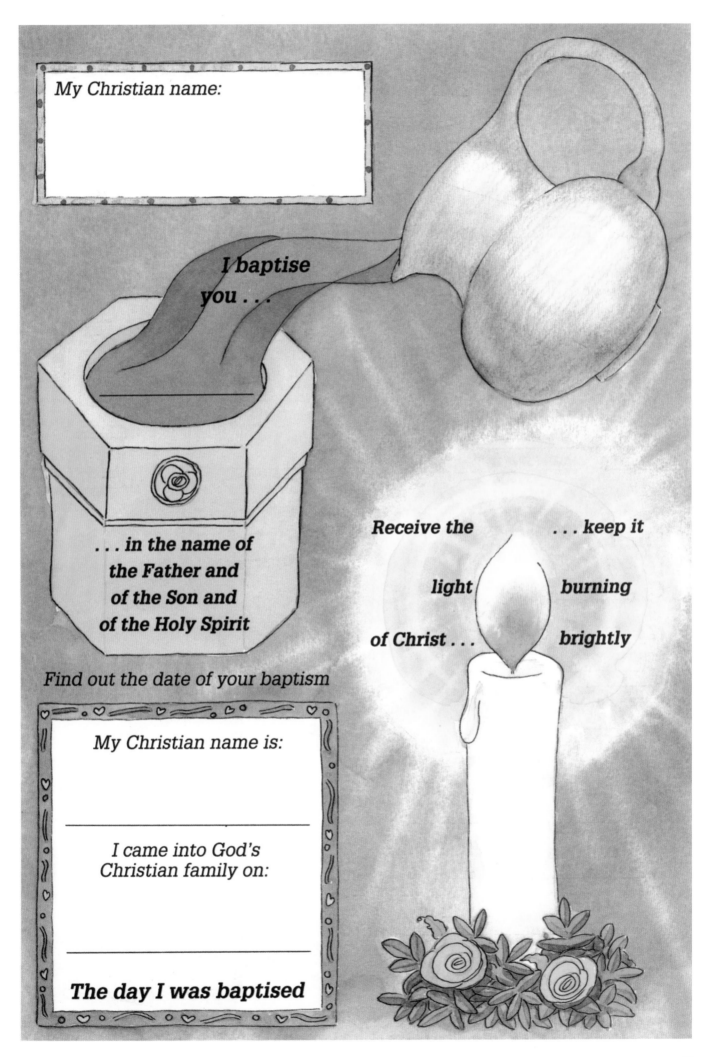

My Christian name:

I baptise you . . .

. . . in the name of the Father and of the Son and of the Holy Spirit

Find out the date of your baptism

My Christian name is:

I came into God's Christian family on:

The day I was baptised

Receive the light of Christ . . .

. . . keep it burning brightly

My Christian Family

God is my father

Me at my baptism!

(Write and colour in the name of the church – draw in the font)

I was baptised at:

Special days in God's family
Sunday

C_____

G_____ F_____

E_____

P_____

Parish

My godparents

Register

Other people at my baptism

Beloved
children
I call you
by name –
you are mine!

God

Stick Jesus'
picture here:

Write his name

Stick your
picture here:

Write your name

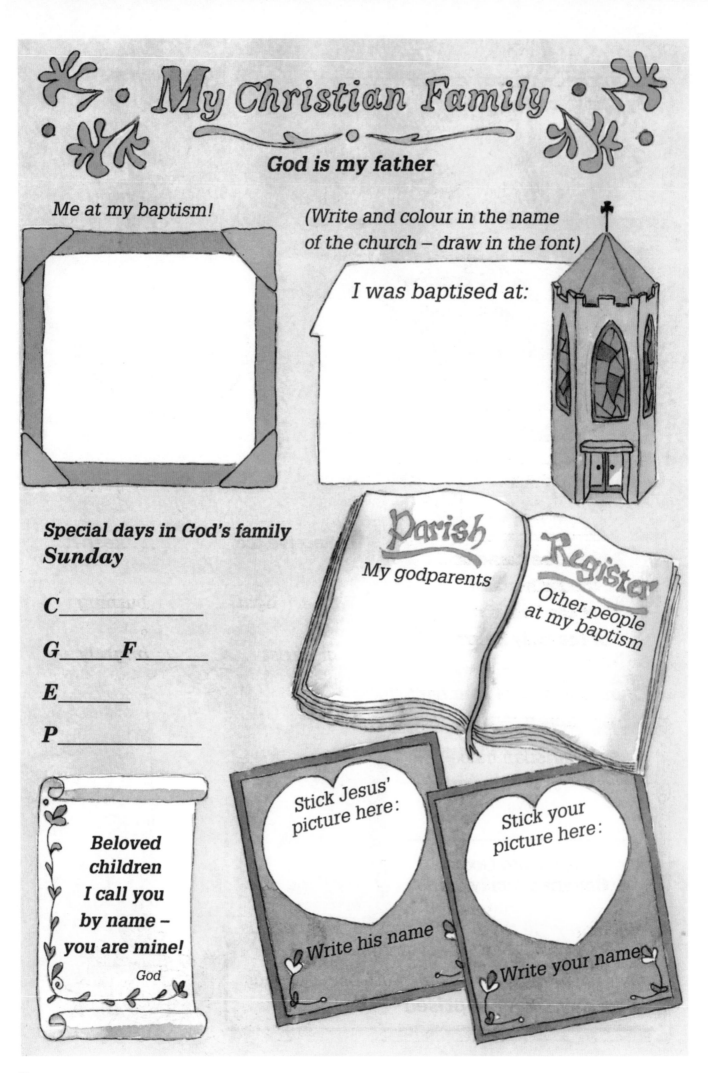

Family Prayer

- Bowl of water.
- Small candle for each person.
- Large candle.
- Scented oil.

Jesus is the Light of the World. In baptism as a sign of this light we were given a lighted candle.

We were asked to take the light of Christ to the whole world by keeping our faith in Jesus alive in our hearts.

In baptism, through water and the Holy Spirit, we were given **new life** through Jesus Christ our Lord.

As a reminder of our baptism we now bless ourselves with water.

Each person blesses themselves with water saying:

In the name of the Father, and of the Son, and of the Holy Spirit. Amen.

In baptism we were anointed with the oil of chrism as brothers and sisters of Jesus, to give us power to live as his family here on earth.

Parent makes the sign of the cross on the head of each one and says:

I anoint you with oil in the name of Jesus, Our Lord. May his power make you strong to be like him.

Give each person a candle lighted from the main candle, which represents Christ, and say:

Receive the light of Christ. Keep it burning brightly. Always live as a child of the light.

Say a special prayer for your First Communion child.
Say together the great prayer of God's family which Jesus taught us: **'Our Father'**

Renewal of baptismal promises . . .

We believe in God, our Father almighty, creator of heaven and earth.
We believe in Jesus Christ, Our Lord: the only son of God, who died to save us.
We believe in the Holy Spirit who lives with us now and for ever. Amen.

This is our faith. This is the faith of our Church. We are proud to believe it.

Family Life

Things we do at home
(draw your family busy at home)

Below: what I best like to do with my family at home

8

With God's Family at Church

Things we do at church
(draw some of them)

*Ideas –
get married;
baptised;
listen to God's
word; pray;
give thanks . . .*

Below: what I like doing best with God's family at church

Family Prayers

Which prayers can you say at home?

When can you pray at home?

Draw in more hands

A morning prayer

A night-time prayer

A meal-time prayer

My own favourite prayer

My prayer for my family

10

Mass Prayers

Write down some prayers you say at Mass

A forgiveness prayer

A whole world prayer. Write your own bidding prayer

A blessing prayer

Jesus' family prayer

A prayer of praise and thanksgiving

My favourite prayer at Mass

Invitation to a Family Celebration

MENU

Prepare the room

Decorate table festively with . . .
- cloth
- candles
- flowers
- place name for each person
- gift for each person
(to be hidden before the meal)

Grace or Blessing

Blessed are you Lord God of all creation. Through your goodness we are here today to share this meal.

Serve the food

Light the candle

Find the gifts

Each one prays in turn . . .

Blessed are you, Lord God of all creation.

Through your goodness I have been given this gift,

which is the work of_____hands.

It will become for me a sign of_____love.

Final Prayer

Blessed are you, Lord God of all creation.

Through your goodness

_____will receive Jesus

in Holy Communion this year

A gift of your love.

A picture of Jesus

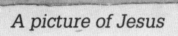

Family Love

Make your own
'How I am loved' page

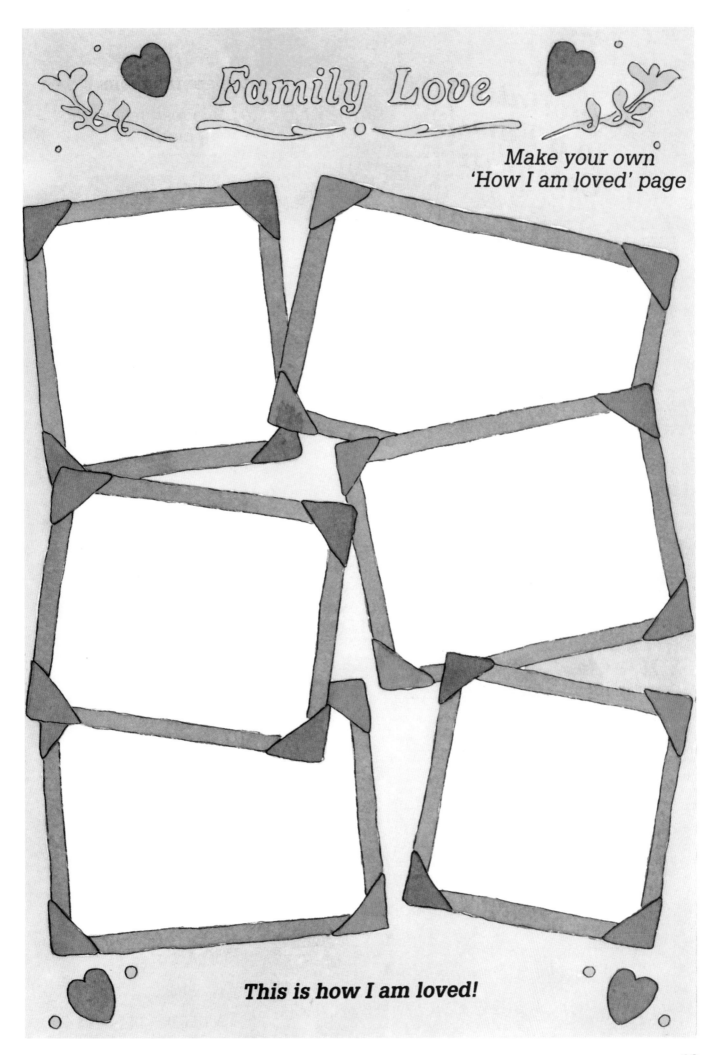

This is how I am loved!

Find the stories
– draw the pictures

Holy Bible

God's love for his family

The Good News: Jesus loves us

Luke 15: 4-7

Luke 15: 8-10

Luke 15: 11-32

Luke 18: 15-17

Me being a loving friend

John 13: 4-17

Holy Bible

Our love for one another

The Good News people love one another

Draw or cut out pictures of people who love and care

This is me being one of those people

Listen with Love at Mass

This is what I hear . . .
(fill in what you hear at Mass)

I love at home when I . . .

I love at school when I . . .

I love out playing when I . . .

16

Liturgy of the Word

Prepare an Altar of the Word
with a cloth, flowers, candles.
Design an attractive cover for your bible.
Place the bible on the altar
open at Matthew 6:24-34

Light the candles

Acclaim the Gospel
Alleluia, alleluia.
We know and believe
in your love O Lord.
Alleluia, Alleluia.

The Holy Gospel given to us by Matthew
Glory to you, Lord Jesus! (Sign forehead, lips and heart with a cross)
Lord, open my mind to hear your word
Open my lips to speak your word
Open my heart to love your word

Jesus told his friends this story . . .
There once lived a king. He was the richest king in the whole
world. His name was Solomon. He lived in a wonderful palace
and he wore the most magnificent clothes that money could buy.
He thought he was the best-dressed man in the world. But no!
Something is better dressed than Solomon – the grass growing
in the fields – the birds flying in the sky – the lovely flowers of
the fields – are dressed more beautifully than Solomon in all his
glory. Why is that? Because our heavenly Father clothes them
and cares for them. And he cares for **you** even more. You are
more special than the grass and the birds and the flowers.
Because you belong to God's very own family.
This is the Gospel of the Lord.

Present your First Communion child with a bible
Let us pray:
Heavenly Father, thank you for loving me more than
the grass and the birds and the flowers.
Help everyone to feel loved . . .

Family continue with their own prayers.   **Say the Hail Mary . . .**

We Celebrate at Home

Fill in your family's special celebration days

January _____

February _____

March _____

April _____

May _____

June _____

July _____

August _____

September _____

October _____

November _____

December _____

Enjoying my favourite celebrations with my family . . .

We Celebrate at Church

Fill in God's family's special celebration days

January _____

February _____

March _____

April _____

May _____

June _____

July _____

August _____

September _____

October _____

November _____

December _____

Enjoying my favourite celebrations with God's family . . .

A Page of Celebrations

Fill with invitations, cards, and pictures of different kinds of celebrations

This year ....
Jesus invites me

_____

to celebrate my first Holy Communion

at _____ Church

on_____ at the _____ Mass

Fill in, then decorate with your favourite colours and patterns

My photo

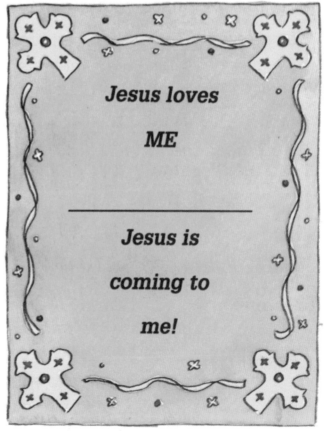

Jesus loves

ME

_____

Jesus is

coming to

me!

Invitation to Supper

Light

Jesus sent Peter and John to Jerusalem to prepare a room where he could invite his friends to a special supper to celebrate freedom.

The Passover Meal

MENU
- Unleavened bread
- Bitter herbs
- Celery • Watercress
- Parsley • Lettuce
- Boiled eggs • Roast lamb
- Chopped apples with honey, nuts, dates, cinnamon
- Sweet red wine

Blessing the wine
Blessed are you Lord God of all creation. Through your goodness we have this wine to share, fruit of the earth and work of human hands.

We thank you for your gift of life.

Hide some bread!

Blessing the bread
Blessed are you Lord God of all creation. Through your goodness we have this bread to share fruit of the earth and work of human hands.
We thank you for your gift of bread.
Host breaks the bread . . .
gives to each person with watercress and salt.

Why do we eat the unleavened bread with bitter herbs and salt?
Because at this meal we remember how God set the Israelites free from slavery.

Read the Passover story
(Exodus 12:1-14)

Bless the wine

Freedom

Have supper – find hidden bread

After dinner

Peace

Bless the wine

Sing
Shalom my friends –
Shalom – shalom

My peace I give to you
My peace I leave with you
Shalom – shalom

Future

Bless the wine

to_____

whom Jesus invites to share his special meal in Holy Communion

I remember when I was . . . (draw how you were!)

I thank you, God, now I am

_____

Colour the children

23

God Gives us a Wonderful World

Make your own wonderful world page, full of your favourite things . . .
(draw; or stick pictures, photos, poems . . .)

At Mass we remember God's great love for us . . .

We give him thanks and praise . . .

The Lord be with you –
and also with you.
Lift up your hearts –
We lift them up
to the Lord.
Let us give thanks to the Lord our God –
It is right to give him thanks and praise.

Holy Holy Holy
Lord God of power and might.
Heaven and earth are
full of your glory.
Hosanna in the highest.
Blessed is he who comes
in the name of the Lord.
Hosanna in the highest.

God's love never ends

God's special
people give him
thanks and praise.

Lord God Almighty Father
It is right always and everywhere to
give you thanks and praise. For the
morning sun over mountains and
seas, for the wind that blows and the
river that flows. For the birds and the
flowers of the field.
I praise and thank you, Lord my God,
for my daily bread – for everything!

I am special

Heaven and Earth are Full of Your Glory

Fill each day with glory

Father, we come to you with praise and thanksgiving

Monday

Tuesday

Saturday

Wednesday

Friday

Thursday

Sunday

Blessed are you Lord, God of all creation Amen

Through Jesus Christ Our Lord

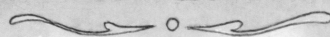

Father, we come to you with praise and thanksgiving

Complete the picture

Jesus:
who, at a meal with his friends . . .

Took **bread,** gave God thanks and praise,

Broke the bread, gave to his friends and said:
'Take, eat.
This is my body, given for you'

Then took the cup filled with **wine** and gave God thanks and praise,

Gave the cup to his friends to drink and said:
'Take and drink. This is the cup of my love for you'

Do this to remember me!

Christ has died –
Christ is risen –
Christ will come again

Amen

Amen

Amen

Through
him, with him,
in him . . .

Amen

. . . in the unity of the Holy Spirit,

all glory and honour is yours

almighty Father,

for ever

and ever

Amen

Amen

With all the angels   ME   and saints

Breaking of Bread

Prepare a table with cloth and candles, bread and wine.

Jesus sent Peter and John
to Jerusalem
to prepare a room
where he could invite
his friends to share a
special supper with him.
It was the Passover supper.

When evening came, Jesus arrived with his friends.
While they were at the table eating, Jesus took some bread and
said the blessing.

**Blessed are you Lord God of all creation.
Through your goodness we have this bread to eat,
fruit of the earth and work of human hands.
It will become the bread of life.**

Jesus broke the bread: he gave it to his friends saying:
Take it . . .
This Is My Body

Break the bread and share it.

Jesus then took the cup filled with wine.
He gave thanks . . .

He gave it to his friends: they all drank. Jesus said:

This Is My Blood
A sign of my everlasting love.
Do This To Remember Me

**Drink the sweet wine.
Sing a favourite hymn.**

**Blessed be God through whose goodness we have shared this
meal and by whose goodness we live . . .**

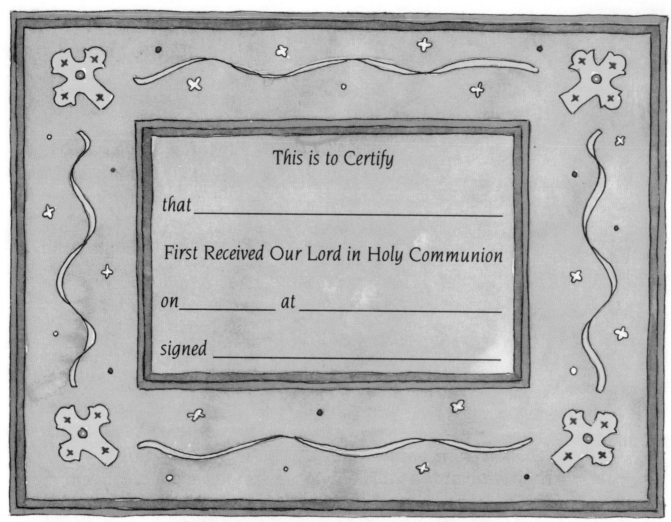

This is to Certify

that _____

First Received Our Lord in Holy Communion

on_____ at _____

signed _____

Ask the priest to sign your certificate

A First Communion photograph

We sang . . .

My prayer to Jesus . . .

*Friends who made their
First Communion with me*

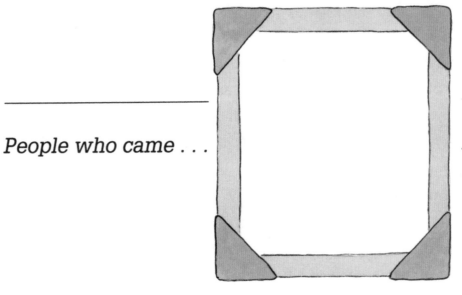

People who came . . .

*How we celebrated
afterwards*

**We go now to live in the
JOY OF THE LORD**

Note to Parents

There was once a time when life was more predictable, and followed a fairly set pattern. And in those once-upon-a-time days people even came to church knowing what to expect! Nothing ever seemed to change.

Liturgical seasons with their colours, green, purple, gold, white and red, flowed through the year, with here and there the blue of Mary days. Festivals and saints days, processions and litanies, devotions and blessings, all had place and meaning celebrating the rhythm of life and the changing seasons of the year.

In today's pace of life, seasons blur into one another. Feast days and festivals come and go unnoticed: the gulf between life and liturgy grows ever wider, and we are in danger of being left with empty ritual and meaningless symbol.

Concerned about this situation, especially with regard to children, the Church issued the Directory on Children's Masses encouraging us to draw upon all that is human to help children to come to a fuller understanding of Liturgy, and in particular the Eucharist, in order to enable them to take part in it more fully and more meaningfully.

Eucharistic preparation is to take place not in isolation, but in the midst of life, with the family, in school, with friends, at church, at play, at meals, at prayer, and in celebration, thus gathering the whole of life up into the one great act of thanksgiving, the Eucharist, where Christ is truly met with joy.

Sr Joan SND